MIRIAM MOSES' SISTER

By Theresa Morin

Illustrations by Ron Wheeler

Miriam liked being a big sister. She never felt lonely when she could play with her little brother and help take care of him.

One day her mother and father told Miriam and her brother Aaron some big news. Soon they would have another new baby brother or sister!

How happy Miriam was when her little brother
Moses was born! When she tiptoed in to see him,
he looked up at her with his round bright eyes.

Miriam thought Moses was so cute, all pink and soft and wiggly. Everyone who came to visit said he was the most beautiful baby ever.

But later, Miriam saw her parents whispering, looking very worried. "What's wrong?" Miriam asked as she climbed onto her mama's lap.

"The Egyptians are looking for baby Hebrew boys," her father told her. "We are Hebrews. We must find a place to hide Moses!"

Miriam knew just the place to keep Moses safe. She ran up to her secret playroom and quickly picked up her toys and swept the floor.

Then she ran back to Mama and Papa and said, "Please, let's hide him in there!"

Moses grew happy and strong in his new little room.

But soon they had to find another hiding place. Moses was growing too big to stay in the little room, so Mama and Miriam wrapped him in a blanket and walked to the river's edge.

They placed him in a basket safe in the bulrushes.
Miriam hid under a shady tree to watch over
him. Hours went by. . . .

Just as she was getting sleepy, Miriam heard singing and laughing. Oh, no! The Egyptian princess was coming with her friends to bathe in the river!

Miriam put a hand over her mouth and watched
with wide eyes as the princess spotted the basket.
Then Moses began to cry!

Miriam watched from her hiding place. She was happy when the princess's kisses stopped Moses from crying, but she came down to the water's edge when the princess said she was going to take Moses home with her.

Miriam had a smart idea. She stepped out where the princess could see her. "Shall I go find a Hebrew woman to take care of the baby for you?" she asked the princess. The princess said yes.

Miriam ran home to get her mother. As they hurried back to the river, Miriam told her everything that had happened.

The princess, not knowing they were Moses' own mother and sister, let them take little Moses home till he grew older!

Miriam was so happy to have baby Moses back home. She helped her mother take care of him every day until he was big and strong.

When the day came for Moses to leave them,
they were all so sad. Moses gave Miriam a big
hug—he knew how she had helped him!

But as they waved good-bye to Moses, they knew they'd see him again. God had told them He had great plans for Moses.